# A Treasury of Islamic Values for Children

*By*
Ameena Golding
Haya Hassan
Hibah Hassan
Xeneb Shah
Zineb Sarah Messaoui

*Edited by*
Tajwar Hassan

# Editor's Note

Allah (swt) has blessed us with four lovely daughters, Hibah, Haya, Areesha and Aaisha. Our children are growing up in a world where advanced technology has led to their exposure to information which is not always in conformance with Islamic values. It is, therefore, imperative that, besides providing them with good schooling, we should also offer them better alternatives to television, the internet, video games, etc. for their spare-time activities, in order to bring them up as good Muslims.

We have lived in Pakistan, Saudi Arabia, the United Kingdom and Egypt, where my children have made good friends, especially in the UK. This small group of friends, of different nationalities and cultures, are bound together only by their common religion, Islam. While browsing one day, it dawned on me that the powerful tool of internet can be used to establish a network of my daughters' friends where they could share moral values in an interesting and amusing way.

While looking for Islamic stories that will convey moral messages for growing children, I came up with the idea of writing a set of stories. We discussed this idea within our network group. Alhamdulillah, the girls were very excited and they willingly took up this challenge as their summer holiday project. To motivate them further, I floated the idea that if the stories were good enough, we would compile them in book form and would try our best to get them published. This was deeply appreciated by the children and according to one child, "it really gave us a great motivation to start the project It happens so often that we work so hard on stories but they end up in bins at school or at home."

The young writers were very excited about the publication and worked hard, day and night, in writing, reviewing and editing their stories. I pray to Allah (swt) that successful publication of their stories will give them further strength and encouragement to channel their

immense talent and energy for the benefit of other children, Ameen.

It is my d'uaa and hope that the commendable efforts of these youngsters will be rewarded by Allah (swt) and that they and other youngsters will be motivated to become better practising Muslims, Ameen.

I would like to take this opportunity to impress upon readers the need to engage our children in activities which are in line with the teachings of Islam, so that they are brought up as successful human beings.

## Acknowledgment

I must express my sincere thanks to Vinni Rahman of Goodword Books for her continuous encouragement and guidance, which helped us greatly in the completing the story writing project.

I greatly appreciate the help of my eldest daughter, Hibah, for spending long hours on drafting and editing of the stories. May Allah (swt) enhance her knowledge and commitment to Islam, Ameen. Special thanks to my husband for his encouragement and support throughout this endeavour. Finally I would like to thank all the parents, mine and the authors', for their prayers to make this project a success.

Tajwar Hassan

# Contents

# The Very Beginning
## BY HIBAH HASSAN

A long, long time ago, there was nothing but a huge dark space. There was no land, no sky, no moon and no sun. Everywhere it was dark and empty.

But Allah, the Merciful, decided to create the world. All He had to say was "Be" and the world was ready.

Allah created seas and lakes and put mountains in place to hold them down and to keep things in balance. He made the mighty mountains tower over the earth and made the seas cover most of the land.

After that Allah created the dry land and He filled it with bushes, trees and lovely flowers. Allah commanded the rain to water the

plants so that they would grow healthy. He created dense rain forests and deserts with very few plants.

Above the earth Allah made the sky. In the sky He created two huge light sources; one was the sun and the other was the moon. He commanded the sun to shine brightly during the day and to fill the world with light and commanded the moon to glow at night. He also created the stars to guide the travellers and to give the moon company.

Allah wanted the world to be perfect, so, out of light, He created the angels to obey Him and to carry His message throughout the world. The angels make sure that everything runs smoothly, that the rain gives water at the right time, that the sun gives its heat and that the wind blows where and when it should blow. Then from fire, Allah created the jinn. He created some good jinns, who are believers, and some bad.

Then Allah made all the animals, big and small. He created every animal you can think of and all the animals you can't think of. He made all kinds of animals — animals that can swim, like fish and octopus, animals that can fly like birds, and animals that can walk on the land on four feet, like monkeys and camels.

The world was a lovely place, filled with colour and happiness. There were many different creatures everywhere.

Finally, Allah decided to make human beings. He took the soil and mixed it up with water like clay. He moulded it into a man's shape and breathed His spirit into it. Allah named the first man Adam. He then created the first woman called Eve.

Allah created a beautiful, perfect world for mankind. He created many different races and people. He created people with black skin, brown skin and white skin. He created short and tall, thin and fat and He created people with different cultures and beliefs. Allah has created this perfect world for the purpose of testing human beings.

# Let's Think

## Lesson Learnt

Allah made this world so perfect that we may know and realize His bounties and blessings and worship Him alone. The life of this world is a test for all human beings and they should work hard towards achieving Paradise in the next life.

## Verses from the Quran

It was He who spread out the earth and placed upon it mountains and rivers, and fruits of every kind in male and female pairs. He drew the veil of night over the day. In all this, truly, there are signs for people who reflect. (13:3)

## Truth from the Hadith

Abu Huraira reported that Allah's Messenger (pbuh) said, Allah the Exalted and Glorious, created the clay on Saturday and He created the mountains on Sunday and He created the trees on Monday and He created the things requiring labour on Tuesday and He created light on Wednesday and He caused animals to spread on Thursday and He created Adam (AS) after 'Asr on Friday; the last creation at the last hour of the hours of Friday, that is between afternoon and night. (Sahih Muslim)

# Chocolate Cake

## BY AMEENA GOLDING

In a little house, in a little town, lived a boy named Ali. He lived with his Mother, Father and his pet cat, Pickles. One day, as Ali came home from school, Ali's Mother noticed Ali chatting to another boy whom she had not seen before.

"Assalamu Alaykum, Ali!" Ali's Mother called to him as he walked up the driveway.

"Wa alaykumus Salam, Mother. Meet my friend Imran. He's just moved into this area. Can he come round to play one day?" Imran asked his Mother.

"He can come round to play now, if it's okay with his parents!"

"Yippee!" exclaimed Ali and Imran.

Imran quickly ran back to his house to ask his Mother if he could play at Ali's house. A few minutes later, Imran returned to Ali's house.

"I am allowed to play at your house!" he said with a smile on his face, as Ali opened the door.

"Cool, my Mum is making my favourite chocolate cake," said Ali as the two ran upstairs to play in Ali's room. The boys were just about to start a game of 'Pick Up Sticks', when Ali's Mother called them down.

"Boys, the chocolate cake is ready." The smell of chocolate cake drifted up the stairs and the boys started to feel very hungry. "Coming, Mum," Ali replied. "We can play the game afterwards," Ali told Imran.

The two boys rushed downstairs and helped Ali's Mother to set the table. Ali's Mother cut two slices of cake and gave the boys a piece each.

"Mum, my piece is smaller than Imran's and he has all the sweets on his piece!" exclaimed Ali.

"Ali, Imran is your guest. In Islam, we must be very kind and generous to our guests, even if it means that sometimes we might not get what we want," said Ali's Mother.

"Um, um, okay! Imran you can have the bigger piece," replied Ali.

From inside, Ali felt a bit upset because chocolate cake was his favourite. The two boys quickly finished the chocolate cake and went back upstairs to play in Ali's room. They were in the middle of playing Pick Up Sticks, when Imran noticed a small, shiny, blue box, underneath Ali's bed.

"Hey Ali, what's in that box under your bed?" asked Imran. "That's my box of shells. I collect shells," replied Ali.

"Wow, that's really cool! Can I have a look?" asked Imran, urging him to open the box.

"Yes, sure," replied Ali, and as he watched, Imran quickly opened the box. "I really like this one," whispered Imran as he gazed at a beautiful red and orange shell that Ali had found when he and his family had gone on holiday to the beach. This shell was one of Ali's favourites, but he remembered what his Mother had told him earlier about being generous to guests.

"Here Imran, keep it." Ali handed the orange shell to Imran. A wide smile spread across Imran's face.

Smiling, he said, "Thank you Ali, you truly are a good friend."

The next day, Ali woke up with a smile on his face and feeling very happy.

"Today is the school trip day. I wonder if Imran will be going too?" Ali thought to himself. Ali quickly got dressed, gulped down his breakfast and rushed to school. He saw Imran standing by the school gates.

"Assalamu Alaykum, Ali!" shouted Imran as Ali reached the school gates.

"Wa alaykumus Salam, Imran. Today is the school trip day. Are you going too?" asked Ali.

"Yes, I am, I'm very excited!" replied Imran.

The two boys ran to the school bus and found their seats. Soon after, Ali and Imran were off on their journey.

"Do you know where we are going, Imran?" Ali asked Imran. "Yes, I do, because my father is the bus driver, but it's a secret. I can't tell you!" exclaimed Imran.

"I hope it's a nice secret," said Ali.

Just as Ali said those words, he suddenly saw the blue sea.

"We are going to the beach! We are going to the beach!" exclaimed Ali. Soon after, the bus stopped and all the children ran out on to the beautiful beach and gazed at the cool sea. Suddenly, Ali saw something on the ground. It was an amazingly glittery red shell! Even more beautiful than the one he had given to Imran. Ali picked up the shell, smiled to himself and thanked Allah for rewarding him for being kind to Imran.

"Alhamdulillah," Ali whispered to himself as he ran to the shore to play with Imran. The two were the best of friends from that day on.

# Let's Think

## Lesson Learnt

If you are generous and kind, Allah will always be kinder to you and reward you with His blessings.

## Verses from the Quran

As for one who gives [to others] and fears [God], and believes in the truth of what is right, We will pave his way to ease. (92:5-7)

Never will you attain to righteousness unless you spend for the cause of God out of what you cherish; and whatever you spend is known to God. (3:92)

## Truth from the Hadith

The Prophet Muhammad (pbuh) said: "He whose property exceeds his needs, let him support the one whose property does not meet his needs, and he whose food exceeds his needs, let him share it with those who do not have food." (Fiqh-us-Sunnah)

# Nuh and the Ark

## BY HAYA HASSAN

Long, long ago there lived some evil people in the beautiful land of Mesopotamia, who prayed to idols instead of praying to the one God (Allah). Allah gave them many things, like beautiful lands, houses and a lot of wealth. But they did not thank Allah or share their wealth with the poor and needy. Allah was very unhappy with them and decided to send a messenger to teach them about Islam.

From among the people, Allah chose one very nice, kind man, named Nuh (Noah) as His prophet and messenger. The Prophet Nuh(AS) was very gentle and trustworthy. He guided the people to the right path, taught them to pray to Allah and to be kind and generous to the needy. But the people were very bad and unkind to him and refused to follow his teachings. They laughed at him and made fun of him. Only some poor people listened to his teachings and followed them.

The Prophet Nuh (AS) told the rich people that he did not want their money or favour , as it was only Allah who could reward people. He knew that Allah would reward his followers and he warned the

evil people of punishment from Allah. The leaders of the town were against the Prophet Nuh(AS) and challenged him by saying, "If what you say is true, then bring upon us the punishment you warn us about." He replied that it was only Allah who could punish anyone and then there would be no escape.

One day, Allah ordered the Prophet Nuh(AS) to build an Ark. He and his followers trusted Allah's wisdom and obeyed Allah.

That afternoon the Prophet Nuh (AS) started building an Ark with the help of his followers. They worked very hard. People made fun of them for building an Ark in the middle of the desert. But the

Prophet Nuh (AS) and his people continued their hard work and trust in Allah till the Ark was made.

When the Ark was ready, Allah ordered the Prophet Nuh (AS) to gather a male and female of each type of animal. He called all the animals in pairs to board the Ark. There were horses, monkeys, giraffes, koalas, spiders and many more. Also, all the good people, who followed the teachings of the Prophet Nuh(AS) were called.

When all the animals had boarded the Ark, it sailed. All of a sudden, black clouds covered the sky like a thick blanket. It started to rain heavily and huge waves crashed across the Ark.

The waves got bigger and bigger and swallowed the evil and unkind people. Their houses were destroyed and nothing was left except the mighty waves.

It rained and rained for days but the mighty Ark sailed over the crashing waves, which were higher than the mountains. Then, after forty days, Allah commanded the sky,

'O sky! Clear of clouds!' At last the rain stopped, the sea became calm and the Ark sailed smoothly and stopped on Mount Judi. All the animals were delighted and cheered in excitement. All on board thanked Allah for saving them from the severe storm.

Allah saved the good and pious people and all sorts of animals, both big and small, that we find today in jungles and zoos. Some animals went back to the jungles, some to the deserts and some to the mountains. The birds flapped their wings and flew up into the sky. The Prophet Nuh (AS) and his people thanked Allah and started a new life and lived happily according to the teachings of Allah.

# Let's Think

## Lesson Learnt

One should always obey Allah. Allah protects the righteous and destroys the wicked people. The evil cannot win against Allah's plan.

## Verses from the Quran

We sent Nuh to his people. He said, 'O my people, worship God; you have no other god but He. I fear for you the punishment of a dreadful Day,' but the leading men of his people said, 'Truly, we see that you are obviously lost in error!' Said [Nuh], 'O my people! I am not in error. Indeed, I am a messenger from the Lord of the Worlds. I am conveying my Lord's messages to you and giving you sincere advice. I know things from God that you do not. (7:59-62)

Earth swallow up your water, O sky, be clear of clouds. (11:44)

Before him Nuh cried out to Us, and We heard his prayer. We saved him and his entire household from a great distress. We helped him against his people who rejected Our revelations. They were surely a wicked people, so We drowned them all. (21:76, 77)

## Truth from the Hadith

Abu Sa'eed Khudri narrates that the Prophet said, When Nuh and his nation will come, Allah will ask, 'Did you convey My message to the people'?

He will reply: 'Yes, My Lord.'

Then He will ask the same question to his nation. They will reply: 'No, no prophet came to us.'

Then God will say to Nuh: 'Who will bear witness for you?' He will say: 'Muhammad and his nation.' Then we will bear witness that he conveyed the God's message to his people. (Al-Sahih Al-Bukhari)

# InshaAllah

## BY HIBAH HASSAN

One dull, rainy day Laila was sitting on the sofa doing nothing. When her Dad came in, Laila said,

"Dad… I'm so bored! There's nothing to do, and even the TV isn't working!"

He said, "Let's think of something good and useful to do. You know, time is very precious and we should spend our time doing meaningful things rather than wasting it on watching TV."

"But Daaad… I don't know what to do. Please help me to think of something."

He sat down next to her and said, "Hmm, Laila, how many Surahs have you learned from the Quran?"

"Only five, but what does that have to do with this?" asked Laila.

"Laila if you learn five more Surahs, then I promise I'll buy you the new 'walking and talking' doll from the toy shop, InshaAllah!"

19

Laila got very excited and gave him a big hug and ran off to find her copy of the Quran.

The next day in school when it was playtime, Laila and her friends Dana and Yasmeen were sitting on the grass, waiting for their turn on the swings.

Laila remembered her Dad's words and said happily, "Guess what my Dad said?"

"What?" asked the girls.

"He said that when I learn five more Surahs, he will buy me the new 'walking and talking' doll from the toy shop!"

Yasmeen smiled really widely and exclaimed,

"Laila, you are so lucky, you will be the first in the whole class to have that doll… everyone wants to buy it!"

But Dana wasn't smiling, she said,

"Laila, you didn't say, 'InshaAllah'. You should always say InshaAllah. If you don't say it, then maybe you won't get the doll!"

"Why not? My Dad promised me!" said Laila.

Yasmeen said, "Do you know what InshaAllah means? It means 'If Allah wills' and we all know that everything happens only if Allah wants it to."

"Don't worry, I don't need to say InshaAllah this time. My Dad never breaks his promises," said Laila confidently…

For a whole week Laila spent her spare time learning her five new Surahs and on Friday she ran down for breakfast with a huge smile on her face.

"Daddy, Daddy! I have learned all the Surahs you asked me to learn!"

When she recited all of the Surahs without any mistakes, her Dad said,

"Well done, Laila, I am very happy and so is Allah. InshaAllah, I will take you to the toyshop tomorrow after the Zuhr (noon) prayer. Now hurry up or you will be late for school."

In the playground, later in the day Laila told Yasmeen and Dana what her Dad had promised, and when it was her turn on the swings, she excitedly jumped on and started swinging as high as she could. Everyone was cheering for her; she was going so fast and so high!

But then suddenly, Laila screamed really loudly and fell off the swings with a huge bump. She lay there crying her knees were bleeding and she couldn't move her arm. Dana ran to get the nurse and Yasmeen rushed to her injured friend.

The nurse called Laila's Mum and told her that Laila's arm looked broken and Laila was taken to hospital.

The next week when Laila's arm was better, she returned to school. On the bus, Dana asked her, "How is your arm? You must have had a good time playing with your doll."

Laila replied, "I couldn't go to the toy shop because all weekend I was in the hospital! But, InshaAllah, my arm is getting better and I will go next weekend, InshaAllah!"

Dana smiled, "I am sure you will never forget to say InshaAllah in the future."

# Let's Think

## Lesson Learnt

InshaAllah means 'if Allah wills'. This is to indicate that everything is in Allah's hands. Nothing can happen without His will. So always remember to say InshaAllah when saying anything that you plan to do.

## Verses from the Quran

Never say of anything, 'I shall certainly do this tomorrow,' without adding, 'if God so wills.' Remember your Lord whenever you might forget and say, 'I trust my Lord will guide me to that which is even nearer to the right path than this.' (18:23-24)

## Truth from the Hadith

The Prophet (pbuh) said, "And never say of anything, I shall do such and such a thing tomorrow, except with the saying 'If Allah wills!' (InshaAllah). And remember your Lord when you forget." (At-Tabarani)

# Habil and Qabil

## BY XENEB SHAH

In the beginning, when there was nothing in this world, Allah decided to create the first man, named Adam (AS) and He also created the first woman, Hawwa (Eve), to give him support and company. The Prophet Adam(AS) and his wife started their lives happily on earth.

Imagine, if you can, what the earth would have been like at that time. An amazing place with no human beings, no traffic, no pollution and no noise. Wow! What a cool place it would have been! Since there were no other people, there were no schools, no markets, no teachers... it must be a serene and peaceful place.

After some time, the Prophet Adam and Hawwa had two baby sons. They named them Habil(Abel) and Qabil(Cain). When they grew up, Qabil, the elder brother became a farmer and he grew lots of vegetables in his fields. Habil, the younger brother, became a shepherd and he took care of all the sheep and the cute baby lambs. While Habil was a good man and loved Allah, Qabil was a mean person and did not fear Allah.

One sunny day, they both decided to make a sacrifice to please Allah. Habil took the best animals he had, while Qabil took his crops. They put their sacrifice in a high place. It was known that if a fire came down from the heavens and burnt the offering to ashes, it was a sign that Allah was pleased. After a while a spark of light came and burnt Habil's offerings to ashes. That was a sign that Allah accepted his sacrifice but rejected Qabil's sacrifice. Qabil's failure made him feel jealous of his younger brother. Instead of realising his

own mistake, he got very angry with his innocent brother. Habil tried his best to explain to his brother that it was because he did not love and fear Allah that his offering had been rejected. But as Qabil was rude and arrogant, he did not listen to his brother and took this as a big insult. He told his brother that he would kill him. Habil did not shout back, but just said calmly, "Even if you kill me, I will not do anything, for I am scared of Allah, the Lord of all the Worlds."

This does not mean that Habil was a coward. He was, in fact, a brave person, but he knew that human beings should not fight among themselves. Qabil was full of arrogance and anger. He killed his innocent brother Habil.

No sooner had he done such a bad deed, that he began to change. Qabil's anger slowly cooled down. He then realised what a big mistake he had made. Then he felt sorry and regretted his bad deed. For hours he sat near his brother's dead body, ashamed and very sad. In deep sorrow, he asked himself what he should do with Habil's dead body.

After a while, Allah sent down a crow, which landed on the ground near Habil's dead body. The crow started scratching the earth to make Qabil understand that he should bury his younger brother's body under the ground. Qabil thought that he was worse than the crow, as he was not even able to hide his brother's body.

# Let's Think

## Lesson Learnt

This story gives us food for thought. We realise that arrogance, jealousy and anger take us away from the path of Allah and instead lead us into sin. We also come to know that human beings should never fight with each other.

## Verses from the Quran

Relate to them, the true story of the two sons of Adam. When they both presented an offering, it was accepted from one of them and not from the other. The latter said, 'I shall kill you!' The former said, 'God accepts [things] only from the righteous. If you raise your hand to kill me, I will not raise mine to kill you. I fear God, the Lord of the Universe." (5:27, 28)

Whoever killed a human being—except as a punishment for murder or for spreading corruption in the land—shall be regarded as having killed all mankind, and that whoever saved a human life shall be regarded as having saved all mankind. Our messengers came to them with clear signs, but many of them continued to commit excesses in the land. (5:32, 33)

## Truth from the Hadith

Abdullah narrated that the Messenger of Allah said, 'Whenever a person is killed unjustly, there is a share from the burden of the crime on the first son of Adam for he was the first to start the tradition of killing'. (Al-Sahih Al-Bukhari)

# Caring For Elders

## BY ZINEB SARAH MESSAOUI

Fatima was a pretty girl, twelve years of age and lived in England with her parents, her twin brothers, Dawud and Sulayman, and her grandmother.

Fatima's school was going on a school trip to Wales for a week. She was so excited that she buzzed around her house not knowing what to do with herself.

"Fatima, come and help me prepare your luggage." called her mother.

Fatima obeyed and went running to her room. She was very busy when she heard her grandmother asking for her: "Fatima, where are you? Come here, I would like to tell you something." "Grandma, I'm busy," groaned Fatima.

"Listen to your grandmother Fatima, you should always respect your elders," scolded her mother.

Fatima grumblingly, trudged over to her grandmother's room. There, her grandma gave her plenty of advice for her school trip: "Never cross the road on your own, never go with a stranger, be careful not to forget a jumper when you're going to cold places, etc..." She was also very concerned about her going without her parents.

"Grandma, I know all that. Stop being so scared about me. You're really annoying!" shouted Fatima. She stomped off back to her

own room. Her grandmother stood there, hurt and saddened by the things her granddaughter had said and the way she had spoken to her. She remembered her granddaughter seven years ago:

"I love you, Grandma," exclaimed the little five year old Fatima to her. She smiled and gave the little girl a kiss. "I will love you and respect you forever," said the little girl, hugging her grandmother."

"I hope so, my dear, I hope so," her beloved grandma had replied...

She went and talked about it to Fatima's mother. Her mother wanted to punish Fatima, but her grandmother wanted to do it another way... That day after the night prayer, Isha, Fatima's mother told everyone to sit around her on the carpet. "I'm going to tell you a story," she announced. Excitement buzzed through the air, for the children's mother always had very interesting stories to tell.

"It is a hadith. You know what is a hadith? It is something the Prophet did or said during his life time. The Prophet had many followers; we call them his companions because they always stayed with him. One day they heard him say: "May his nose be rubbed in

29

the dust, may his nose be rubbed in the dust, may his nose be rubbed in the dust." The companions were astonished. "O Prophet, who should be humiliated in such a way?" they asked. "It is someone who did not look after his old parents when he had the means to. Allah sent him to hellfire," she ended.

Then Fatima's father, who had been listening, added another hadith: "He who does not respect the elders amongst us and is not merciful to the young is not one of us," he said. "Which means that he is not worthy to be part of the Ummah, the Muslim community." "So, you see, children, you should always look after and respect your elders," said the parents together. "Yes, Mum," said Fatima and her brothers. "Even though maybe sometimes we don't understand our elders, because they have different ways of thinking, we should still respect them. The Quran, our holy book gives a high status to them."

That night, Fatima had a nightmare. She dreamt that she was in Jahannam (Hell) burning. She could hear her mother's voice telling her to respect her grandmother and see the sad hurt face of her Grandma when she had shouted at her.

She woke up sweating and burst into tears. She remembered all the times her Grandma had stood up for her and given her presents

and helped her. Fatima ran into her grandmother's room. She found her sitting on her bed reading the Quran. "Forgive me, Grandma, forgive me," sobbed Fatima "I promise I will always respect you and love you…" Her grandmother hugged her. "I had already forgiven you, darling. I know that you won't do it again." She made Fatima lie down on her own bed and lulled her to sleep. From then on Fatima kept her word.

# Let's Think

## Lesson Learnt

We must always respect our elders, as they are wiser than we are and have much more experience. Allah has promised a big reward for being kind to elders.

## Verses from the Quran

Worship Allah and join none with Him and do good to parents, kinsfolk, orphans, the needy and neighbours.... (4:36)

Your Lord has commanded that you should worship none but Him, and show kindness to your parents. If either or both of them attain old age with you, say no word of contempt to them and do not rebuke them, but always speak gently to them (17:23)

## Truth from the Hadith

Anas ibn Malik (RA) narrated that the Prophet (pbuh) said, "If a young man honours an elderly man on account of his age, Allah appoints someone to honour him in his old age." (At-Tirmidhi)

One who does not show kindness to our young ones and does not respect our elders is not from amongst us. (At-Tirmidhi)

# Be Kind to Animals

## BY HIBAH HASSAN

One summer's day, a boy named Amr was riding back home from school on his new, shiny bike. He saw a small boy throwing stones at the pigeons in the park. The boy was hitting the birds and hurting them. Amr felt very sad for the birds and asked the boy,

"What is your name and why are you throwing stones at the birds?"

The boy turned around and laughed. "My name is Yousef and I like throwing stones at the birds. It's so much fun! If the birds get hurt, it isn't my fault, they should fly away!"

Amr replied politely, "But it's not kind to throw stones at them and the Prophet (pbuh) was always kind to animals. Islam teaches us never to harm any animal, so please stop it."

But Yousef just laughed and walked away.

The next day Amr found Yousef in the park still throwing stones at the pigeons. All of a sudden, a big pigeon fell from a tall maple tree, hurt by Yousef's stone. Amr quickly ran to the pigeon and said to Yousef angrily, "Look what you've done! This pigeon is hurt badly and she can't fly. Maybe her leg is broken!"

Yousef ran to the pigeon and started crying. He was really upset at what he had done, as he hadn't meant to hurt the bird. He had only been trying to have some fun.

"I'm really very sorry, but what can we do now for the pigeon?" he asked. "We have to save her."

Amr had an idea, "I know! Let's take this mummy bird to the vet in the small animal hospital nearby. Maybe they can help."

The boys took the pigeon into the doctor's room and told the doctor how the pigeon got hurt. The doctor was upset with Yousef but when he saw how sorry Yousef was, he thought for a minute and smiled.

"Lift the bird up and put her on my bird table, please," he said.

Amr carefully placed the bird on the table and said, "What will you do to her now? Can you help her?"

The vet replied, "Well, first I have to wrap her up in a warm towel so that she won't be cold. Then I will check her thoroughly."

When the vet tried to wrap the bird up, it hopped off the table and sat on Yousef's head! Everybody felt relaxed and laughed, even Yousef!

The vet pressed different parts of the pigeon's body, frowned and said,

"Aha, look here, she has broken her wing, which is why she can't fly properly."

He looked at the boys and said, "Don't worry, she will be okay in a couple of weeks, but I have to keep her here in my hospital so that I can look after her properly."

Both Amr and Yousef thanked the vet and went back into the park to get their bikes.

When they reached the park, Yousef suddenly heard a soft cheeping sound from up in the tree. He quickly climbed up the tree like a monkey and peeped into the small brown nest. Inside the nest

he found two baby pigeons! "Come quickly, Amr! Look what I've found! These baby birds are so cute, but they look very hungry! I wonder where their mother is?"

"Oh, I think the hurt pigeon was their mother," replied Amr.

"I've hurt her and it's all my fault!" wept Yousef.

Amr, seeing Yousef crying, felt very sorry for him and said, "Come on, help me get this nest down. We can take the birds to my house and look after them! Let's go now!"

As soon as the two boys reached Amr's house, Amr ran up to his mother's room, gave her a hug and said,

"Assalamu Alaykum Mum, this is my friend Yousef. Please can you come downstairs because we want to show you something cool."

Amr's mother walked downstairs and into the living room, and when she saw the baby pigeons, she said,

"MashaAllah, look at these beautiful birds that Allah has made, but where is their mother?" she asked.

"Mum, the pigeon's mother is at the vet's clinic," explained Amr. "She's hurt, but can we please look after her babies?"

"Yes, of course you can, Amr, but it's a big responsibility. Are you sure you two are ready to take it on?"

"Yes, we are sure," replied the boys simultaneously.

"Come on then, let's go into the garden and dig up some worms to feed the birds!" said the mother.

The boys went into the garden, took spades out of the shed and dug up some soil. Yousef picked up a worm and it wiggled on his palm. He said, "This is so much fun! I'd love to do this every day!"

Amr cried, "Look at this one, it's as long as my shoe! Come on, let's give it to the birds!"

Mum brought a big box from the garden shed and both boys filled it up with straws and soft grass to make a nest for the baby birds.

Every day after school, for two weeks, Yousef came to Amr's house to take care of the birds. They fed them worms, regularly changed the water and once a week cleaned the box. The birds started to grow bigger and the box nest was no longer big enough for them. The birds needed a proper nest in the trees to give them more space to learn to fly.

Amr didn't have any trees in his garden and they didn't know what to do. They didn't want to put the birds back in the park because they were not sure that little birds could survive without their mother. Both boys loved taking care of their birds.

Yousef had an idea. Maybe he could keep the pigeons in his garden. There were loads of trees and plenty of flowers. They both liked Yousef's idea.

"I promise I will take care of them," said Yousef to Amr. "Finally, I'll have some pets to look after, and they're so lovely! After all, they are my responsibility, because they are in this condition due to me."

So the next day, they carried the birds to Yousef's garden and placed them in a nest that Yousef had made with his Mum's help. They moved the birds into their new nest with some food and water. Yousef took good care of them.

Amr and Yousef spent a lot of time together playing with their birds. One day Amr said to Yousef, "You should always be kind to animals. You have lots of human friends but it's nice to have some animal friends too!"

# Let's Think

## Lesson Learnt

One should be always kind to animals and birds and remember that Allah does not like those who are cruel to His creation. So love Allah's creation and be kind to all and Allah will also love you.

## Verses from the Quran

There is not an animal that moves about on the earth, nor a bird that flies on its two wings, but are creatures like you. We have left out nothing in the Book-they shall all be gathered before their Lord. (6:38)

## Truth from the Hadith

"He who takes pity even on a sparrow and spares its life, Allah will be merciful to him on the Day of Judgement." (At-Tabarani)

# The Prophet Yunus and the Whale

### BY HIBAH HASSAN

A long, long time ago, in the city of Nineveh, there lived a man called Yunus (Jonah). He was a prophet of Allah. Allah sent the Prophet Yunus(AS) to the people to teach them about Allah, so that they would give charity and would be kind to everyone.

But the people of Nineveh did not listen to the Prophet Yunus(AS). They laughed at him and were very unkind. They continued to worship several gods instead of the one true God. The Prophet Yunus(AS) got angry with the people and went away from them. He went to the seaside and got on to a big boat to go somewhere else where people would listen to him.

When the ship was out in the middle of the sea, it suddenly became dark and windy. A terrible storm started and all the men on the ship got scared that the ship would sink.

They decided to make the ship lighter by throwing someone overboard. They chose the Prophet Yunus(AS). They caught hold of him and threw him out of the boat into the dark and scary sea. The Prophet Yunus(AS) was very scared and started to swim, but a big blue whale came up to him and swallowed him in one big gulp!

He went down into the whale's tummy. It was very damp and gloomy in there.

Inside the whale, Prophet Yunus felt very frightened and prayed

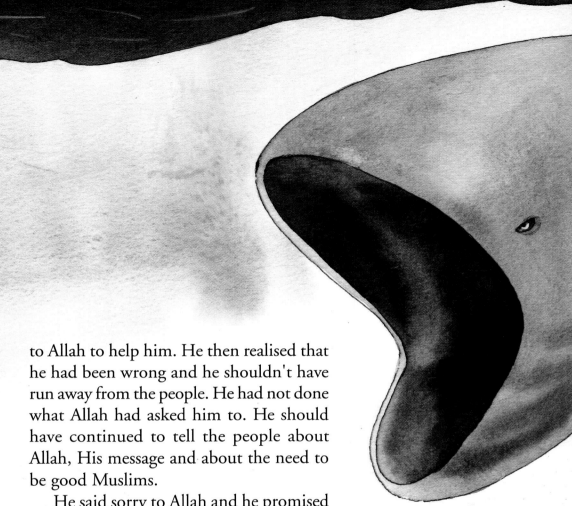

to Allah to help him. He then realised that he had been wrong and he shouldn't have run away from the people. He had not done what Allah had asked him to. He should have continued to tell the people about Allah, His message and about the need to be good Muslims.

He said sorry to Allah and he promised always to listen to Him.

Allah is very kind and when he heard the Prophet Yunus's (AS) prayer, He told the whale to take him to the shore. The whale blew the Prophet Yunus (AS) out of her spout and he landed on a stretch of soft golden sand.

The Prophet Yunus (AS) rested for a while, drank some water and ate some delicious fruits from a tree and then he went back to his people.

When he got back to his people, he told them all about Allah and about the beauties of heaven and the horrors of hell and how one had to be responsible for one's deeds. And then a very surprising thing happened. Everyone started to listen to the Prophet Yunus (AS) and they became good Muslims.

The Prophet Yunus (AS) was very happy that he had finally been able to obey Allah and that the people of Nineveh had become good and caring Muslims.

# Let's Think

## Lesson Learnt

A Muslim should never become hopeless but should be patient and continue to do the work assigned by Allah and always seek help from Him. Allah always forgives those who sincerely seek His forgiveness and repent.

## Verses from the Quran

Jonah (Yunus), too, was one of the messengers. He fled to the overloaded ship. And then they cast lots and he was the one who lost, and the fish swallowed him while he was blaming himself. Had he not been one of those who acknowledged the glory of God, he would certainly have remained inside the fish till the Day of Resurrection. But We caused him to be cast forth on to the beach, sick as he was, and We caused a gourd tree to grow over him. (37:139-146)

Remember the man in the whale [Jonah] when he went away in anger, thinking that We had no power over him. But he cried out in the darkness, 'There is no deity but You. Glory be to You! I was indeed wrong.' So We heard his prayer and delivered him from sorrow. Thus shall We deliver the true believers. (21:87-88)

## Truth from the Hadith

Abdullah Ibn Abbas narrated that the Prophet said, 'No slave (of Allah) should say that I am better than Yunus bin Matta.' So the Prophet mentioned his father's name with his name. (Al-Sahih Al-Bukhari)

# Dry Bread and Water

## BY HIBAH AND HAYA HASSAN

Early in the morning, in a little house in America, the Hassan family was having breakfast. Of the three children, Omar was the eldest. He was 9 years old and had black hair. The twins, Sara and Zara were 4 years old and had brown curly hair.

They were usually smiling but, at the dining table, the children were cross.

"Mummy, I don't want pancakes! I want cereal!" shouted Sara loudly.

"Mum, I don't like orange marmalade. I want strawberry jam," moaned Omar.

"Sorry Omar, we haven't got any strawberry jam. Now eat your breakfast quickly," replied Mum.

Zara, the naughty one, threw her plastic plate on the floor and threw her spoon at Omar's head.

"Mum, I don't like this pancake. It's too hard!" said Zara and she crossed her arms.

Their mother sighed, scolded the children, picked up the plates and spoons and gave everyone some orange juice.

"But mum, the juice is too sour!"

"No, it is too sweet!"

"It's not even cold, Mum!" A series of complaints started.

Their mother was not happy with the ungrateful attitude of her children, but she didn't say anything. She kissed the children goodbye and watched them get on the bus.

The children went to school with their new shiny lunch boxes packed with yummy food. But when they returned from school, Mum noticed that they hadn't finished their lunch.

The children ran upstairs and went to their rooms. They played and watched TV.

At 6.30 p.m., the door opened and Dad walked in after a long

day at work. The children greeted him happily, shouting, "Assalamu Alaykum, Dad!"

"Wa alaykumus Salam children. Come to the dining room. Your mother needs some help in setting the table," Dad replied.

The children quickly set the table and everyone sat down to dinner, which was spaghetti with meatballs. The grumbling started all over again. Sara and Zara moaned that they liked spaghetti but not with meatballs. Omar said that he liked the meatballs but not the spaghetti.

Hearing the children whining, Dad said, "Children, be grateful for what you have and hurry up and finish your food."

The children saw that Dad was getting cross so they ate quickly and ran upstairs.

When the children were upstairs, it was Mum's turn to complain to Dad.

"The children are never happy with their food. They are always grumbling and are never grateful. What shall we do?"

Dad had an idea, "Why don't you tell the children about the poor who don't have any food and maybe then they will eat."

"But what if they still don't eat their food, what shall we do then?" asked Mum.

Dad thought for a while and said something quietly to Mum. She smiled and agreed with Dad's clever idea.

The next day began the weekend. When the children came down for breakfast, Dad and Mum talked to them about how poor children felt when they didn't have any food and were very hungry. Mum told them that the Prophet Muhammad (pbuh) told us that, Allah (swt) loved the people who fed and helped the poor and needy. The children agreed and promised that they would give a lot of food to the less fortunate, so they wouldn't be hungry.

The children ate their breakfast, forgetting about what their mother had explained and still complained about their food. The children played all day, came downstairs and asked their mother what was for lunch.

"Sorry children, we don't have much food today, because I gave it all away to the poor," said Mum. "We'll have plain bread with water."

The children were shocked. They couldn't believe what Mum had just said.

They didn't say anything, and sat down and started to eat.

"Eew, this bread has no butter," said Sara.

"Remember children, poor people don't have enough money to buy butter so I gave them our butter," Mum explained.

So for lunch the children had to eat the bread with water. At dinnertime, the children hopefully thought there would be something

nice to eat. But they were surprised to see it was again bread and water.

The children realised their ungratefulness and sat with their parents after dinner. They promised that they would be thankful to Allah, they would not complain about food and would eat everything.

The Hassan children had learnt the value of food and the feelings of the less fortunate people suffering from hunger. From that day on, the children never complained and finished their lunch in school as well as their meals at home. They also helped the poor by sharing their food and other things with them.

# Let's Think

## Lesson Learnt

This story explains the importance of the food that we sometimes take for granted. Allah loves the people who thank Him for his blessings and share what they have with less fortunate people. So eat your food with good grace and be thankful to God.

## Verses from the Quran

Believers, eat the wholesome things, which We have provided for you and give thanks to God, if it is Him you worship. (2:172)

## Truth from the Hadith

"One who has eaten some food and then says, 'All praise is for Allah, who has given me this food to eat and provided for me without any effort or power on my part,' will have his sins forgiven." (At-Tirmidhi)

# Thank You Aliya

## BY XENEB SHAH

15th August, 08

Dear Diary,

I am so excited! Do you know why? Well, I have finally got a friend in my neighbourhood. You know how I used to feel when I didn't have any friends. I never liked the company of those crazy boys, but now, thank God, I've got a friend. Her name is Aliya. Now we'll play together, swim together and do so many things. Oh diary, it's getting late and I am sleepy, Sorry... see you later.

19th August, 08

Dear Diary,

Aliya did something weird today. We were riding our bikes when we accidentally crashed into a puppy. I told her to run fast before anyone caught us. But she completely ignored me, picked up the puppy and carried it home. Then she put some ointment on it and took care of it until it became better and then we returned the puppy to its owner. Thank God, he didn't

scold us; otherwise we'd have been in big trouble. Later I asked her why she had done that when there was no one to catch us. She replied that we might think that no one was watching us, but Allah watched us all the time. Isn't that strange diary that she knows more about Allah than I do?

28th August '08

Dear Diary,

Aliya is different from all the girls I know. You know what she did today? We were playing at her house today while her maid was ironing her clothes. Her maid was so foolish that she burned her new dress. I was so angry, but Aliya did not scold her at all. She just said, "Its okay, but be careful next time."

I asked how it was okay when she had burnt her new dress. Why hadn't she shouted at her? I even told her that she should ask her Mom to fire such a careless maid, but she replied that if we were kind to our servants, Allah would be kind to us. Our Prophet (pbuh) was very forgiving and kind to his servants.

Oh, my dear diary! Why on earth does she know so much? I think I need to ask my Mom to tell me more about the Prophet (pbuh)

2nd September, 08

Dear Diary,

Can you believe that Aliya is fasting? When we were playing outside, I got thirsty and ran to get some water. Aliya asked me if I was fasting. I told her I couldn't fast as I felt thirsty and hungry (In fact, no one fasts in our home. You know that, diary, don't you? But I did not tell Aliya this.) She said when

you leave eating and drinking for Allah's sake, He helps you and you don't feel any difficulty. What strange ideas!

P.S. I forgot to tell you she has given me some Islamic books and I have learned a lot about my religion, but still I can't fast, diary. Or should I? What do you say?

27th Ramadan 1429H

Dear Diary,

Surprised with the date? Yes, you should be. Alhamdulillah, (Praise be to God) I am a different person now. I say prayers five times a day, keep fasts and I try to be kind to others. Aliya is a wonderful

49

friend. She has helped me to practice my religion. You know, diary, I have opened an account. It is not an account where you keep money. It's an account where you keep your good deeds, so that you may go to Paradise (Jannah) and this is my own idea not borrowed from Aliya!

# Let's Think

## Lesson Learnt

We should always try to be in the company of good and righteous people who can help us to become better Muslims and human beings.

## Verses from the Quran

Keep yourself attached to those who call on their Lord, morning and evening, seeking His pleasure; and do not let your eyes turn away from them, desiring the attraction of worldly life; and do not obey one whose heart We have made heedless of Our remembrance, one who pursues his own whims and becomes dissolute. (18:28)

Do not incline toward those who do wrong, lest the Fire touch you. For [then] you would have none to protect you from God, and you will not be helped. (11:113)

## Truth from the Hadith

The example of a good companion and a bad one is the bearer of musk and the worker on the bellows. A bearer of musk would give you some, you might buy some from him, or you might enjoy the fragrance of his musk. The worker on the bellows, on the other hand, might spoil your clothes with sparks from his bellows, or you might get a bad smell from him." (Al-Bukhari and Muslim,)

# The New Trend

## BY HIBAH HASSAN

As the teacher had left the classroom for a while, Rana stood up and said boastfully, "Look everyone, my Dad bought me the new heeleys. They are so expensive! I am the first one in the class to get them. They have wheels on the bottom. Aren't they cool? Zaina, Madiha, Hafsa and Nadia, you should get them too!" Then the teacher came back into the room and Rana quickly sat down.

It was 3'o clock in the afternoon and Mrs. Salma's class was just finishing. The bell rang and all the girls rushed out of the class. Hafsa slowly walked out of the room looking gloomy. She knew what her mother would say if she asked her for heeleys, 'Hafsa, you already have nice shoes. You should not overspend on clothes and shoes.' Hafsa sighed and walked home.

The next day in the classroom, Hafsa noticed that some other girls like Madiha, Zaina and Yara were also wearing the new heeleys.

But today Rana wasn't wearing the heeleys. She was wearing shiny sandals with lights on them. Hafsa did not bother to hear how much it cost and where Rana had got them from. She wished she could have them but she remembered her mother's words and tried to forget about it.

During the day Rana only talked about her clothes and shoes. The other girls followed Rana around and tried to copy her. When

the school day ended, Hafsa walked home sadder and gloomier than before. On the way home, she met her classmate, Nadia. Both the girls started talking about the class hot topic; 'light-up sandals'.

Nadia told Hafsa that her mother said she couldn't afford to buy the heeleys, as they were very expensive.

Hafsa shared her feelings and said, "You know, I didn't even ask my Mum, because I knew she would tell me I should not copy others in useless things."

"It's not fair, if I don't get the new shoes, maybe Rana and her group won't be my friends," said Nadia, sobbing.

"Don't worry, Nadia, I like you and I will always be your friend, no matter what you wear," comforted Hafsa.

Hafsa and Nadia then split up and went back home by different roads. Hafsa was happier now as she had made a new friend.

When she got home, she saw a huge cake on the dining room table. Her eyes lit up and she ran to her mother.

"Mummy, Mummy, why is there a cake on the table? Is someone coming to visit? Who, Mummy, who is coming to our house?" she asked her mother excitedly.

"Assalamu Alaykum, yes, Hafsa! Your auntie Rummana is coming to stay with us for a few days and you will have lots of fun

with her. I baked this cake to share with her."

Hafsa happily ran upstairs and forgot about everything that had happened in school.

She had a bath, put on some clean clothes, because she knew that the Prophet (pbuh) said you should always be clean and should smell nice.

She said the afternoon prayer, Asr, and started her homework.

She was nearly finished when the doorbell rang. Hafsa leapt up to answer the door. It was her Auntie Rummana. She greeted her auntie with a big hug and for the whole day she had lots of fun with her. She went to bed with a smile on her face.

The next day Hafsa woke up happily and got ready for school.

At school she saw Rana surrounded by a group of girls, including Nadia, showing off her new pink fur coat,

"Yesterday, my parents went to the huge mall, and my Mum bought me this coat. You know my Mum says it cost a lot of money and she says its real fur and she also says it's the new fashion. Zaina, Madiha, Nadia and Hafsa, you have to get one like mine or I won't be your friend," said Rana.

"But Rana, my Mum says that it cost too much money and you shouldn't waste money. But please be my friend anyway, Rana,"

pleaded Nadia.

Rana looked at her, frowned in a mean way and walked off, leaving Nadia crying.

When Hafsa went home she decided that she would do something to help Nadia. At home she pretended that nothing was wrong. But her intelligent auntie Rummana guessed something was up.

When Hafsa and her auntie were alone in the room, she asked. "Hafsa, what is wrong? You do not seem as happy as you usually are. Did something happen at school?"

Hafsa sighed loudly and explained. "Well, there is this girl at school who is the 'leader', and she always wears very expensive things and everyone tries to follow her example, except for a few of us. She is pretty mean to us. I don't know what to do. Can you help me, Auntie Rummana?"

Her Auntie thought for a while and then a smile crept over her face. She whispered something in Hafsa's ear and Hafsa smiled too.

The next day Hafsa came to school with a pretty scarf around her head. She also had a prayer mat in her bag. In the classroom, Hafsa noticed Rana was absent. As she walked in, some of the girls admired her scarf and asked her why she was wearing it.

She told them Allah has asked Muslims to dress nicely and modestly.

"Hafsa, what does modest mean?" asked Zaina.

"The Prophet (pbuh) said that when a girl grows up, she should cover herself properly and cover her hair nicely. Dressing like this is being 'modest' in the eyes of Allah," replied Hafsa confidently.

"Oh, okay, we understand now," replied the girls.

That day, instead of going to lunch, Hafsa went into the spare room and took out her prayer mat and said the noon prayer, Zuhr. After prayers, she joined the other girls for lunch. Hafsa said "Bismillah" (In the name of Allah) and started to eat. All the girls watched her but nobody said anything. When school ended, Hafsa ran home, gave her auntie a big hug and thanked her for the good idea.

The next day Nadia was also wearing a scarf. Mrs. Salma noticed Hafsa and Nadia wearing scarves. She talked during the lesson about the importance in Islam of dressing modestly and being covered up. She also explained that it is not important how you look but it is important how you think and behave. She went on to say how important education in Islam is. Therefore, it is their duty to excel in studies and not in looks, for all that is no more than just a distraction.

The girls in Hafsa's class were very impressed by her and they all realised that Hafsa and Nadia were doing the right thing. Hafsa became very popular and everyone wanted to be her friend. When Rana saw this, she became angry and started to tease Hafsa and Nadia. But they were quite confident in themselves that they were doing the right thing. The two girls did not bother.

The other girls realised that Rana was very mean and they didn't want to copy her any more. Even when Rana got the new 'beach crocs' the other girls were more interested in Nadia's new prayer mat

and in their studies. That day, Rana realised that showing off about money and clothes didn't win friends.

In the next few days, five other girls wore scarves to school, and they all prayed together. After a month, all the girls, including Rana, were wearing scarves and saying the Zuhr prayer together in the spare room and also concentrating more on their studies.

Hafsa and Nadia remained best friends but, instead of being followers, they became leaders.

# Let's Think

## Lesson Learnt

We should do the right things and make friends who bring us closer to Allah. And remember to dress smartly and look nice but, at the same time, look modest. Intelligence is more important than looks.

## Verses from the Quran

Believers do not cancel out your charitable deeds with reminders and hurtful words, like one who spends his wealth only to be seen by people, and not believing in God and the Last Day. (2:264)

Qarun (Korah) was one of Moses' people, but he behaved arrogantly towards them. We had given him such treasures that their very keys would have weighed down a band of strong men. His people said to him, 'Do not exult in your riches, for God does not love the exultant.' (28:76)

## Truth from the Hadith

Abu Mas'ud 'Uqba ibn 'Amr al-Ansari al-Badri reported that the Messenger of Allah (pbuh) said, "Anyone who shows the way to something good has the same reward as the person who does it." (Muslim)

# Zara and the Four-leafed Clover
## BY AMEENA GOLDING

It was a beautiful, sunny day at school. Zara and her best friend Yasmeen were playing on the playground swings, when Zara noticed a group of kids crawling around on a patch of grass. "What are they doing?" whispered Zara to Yasmeen. "I don't know!" replied Yasmeen. "Come on, let's go and have a look," said Zara. So the two girls ran to the patch of grass and saw that the kids were searching around for some green flowers that teacher had called 'clover'. "What are you looking for? Have you lost something?" asked Zara. A boy stood up. "No Zara, we're looking for four-leafed clover. They bring

you good luck. They're really rare, but I found one last week," boasted the boy. "Neat!!!" shouted Zara, as she too joined the other kids to search for this 'lucky' clover. Yasmeen only frowned and said, "Zara, you really shouldn't..." but before she could finish, Zara stood up and shouted, "I've found one! I've found one! Now I'm going to have good luck..."

The next week, all sorts of good things happened to Zara. She found her favourite jumper and her sparkly bracelet. Her Mum bought her a new dress and she won a math's contest at school, but she gave the credit to her clover, rather than to Allah and her own hard work.

A few days after all these good things had happened, all the bad things started happening to her. Zara couldn't find her special clover anywhere! She was really upset. She began to search everywhere but it wasn't anywhere to be found. That wasn't the end of her troubles though. She broke a crystal glass and some plates. She tripped over her book bag and stubbed her toe. She even lost her new sweater. Devastated, she called Yasmeen and told her of her bad day. "Oh Zara! Haven't you learned your lesson yet?" was her friends reply to her awful day. "Yeah, I learned that you should put your four-leaf clover in a treasure chest," said Zara, despite her tears. "Anyway, I was trying to tell you that clover doesn't give you luck. There's no such thing! Everything happens through Allah's will. Did you know that lucky charms are (forbidden) haraam?" She went on, "Just to make you see the truth, I had hidden your clover in the secret pocket of your bag, so dear Zara, the clover was always with you." Zara gasped in reply, Yasmeen went on, "You should not believe in lucky charms, or that they can bring you good or bad luck. Everything really only happens through Allah's will! Believing in lucky charms is like not believing in Allah!"

Zara just gasped again and then ended the phone call by saying, "I didn't realise it was that serious! Well, from now on I'll work hard and never trust on a lucky charm again!" She threw away the clover and kept her promise after that.

# Let's Think

## Lesson Learnt

There is no such thing as good luck charms. Things like these are superstitions. Only believing in Allah is what gives you success, because it is only Allah who is Almighty and all-powerful. Everything happens only because of His will.

## Verses from the Quran

No misfortune can affect the earth or your own selves without its first having been recorded in a book, before We bring it into being. That is easy for God to do....(57:22)

He who turns his back should remember that God alone is self-sufficient and worthy of all praise. (57:24)

## Truth from the Hadith

Allah, You Alone bring good things, You alone avert evil things and there is no might or power but in You. (Abu Dawood). Abdullah Ibn Mas'ud reported that the Prophet (pbuh) said, "Believing in bad omens is a form of idolatry." Ibn Mas'ud added, "It may occur to any one of us, but God clears it away when we rely totally on Him." (Al-Bukhari, At-Tirmidhi, and Abu Dawud)

# The Prophet Sulaiman and Justice

### BY XENEB SHAH

"Sana, have you packed your bag?"

"Yes, Mom, I'm almost done," shouted Sana from upstairs as she put her books into her bag. She came running down to where her parents were waiting ready for the journey. She got into the car.

"Oh Mom, I'm so happy to visit Granny after ages," Sana exclaimed!

"Yes, honey, I know you could not visit her last time because of your exam," her Mom replied.

"It's so nice that Papa has to go on an official trip and you decided to drop me at Granny's home," said Sana.

An hour later they reached the beautiful "Hussaini Cottage", Sana's maternal family home.

"Granny, I am home!" shouted Sana as she entered the beautiful wooden cottage at the top of the hill.

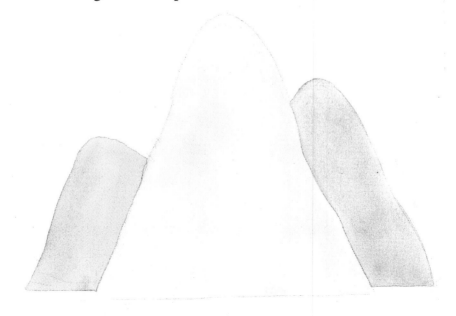

"Oh my baby, I was waiting for you so eagerly!"

Then Sana and her Granny, Mrs. Hussaini, went inside the cottage and Sana's parents left for the town where they had to spend a few days.

"Sana, let's eat lunch and then we'll sit on the balcony and…"

"You'll tell me some wonderful stories, yes Granny?" asked Sana eagerly.

"Why not, darling," replied Granny with a wonderful smile on her face.

Lunch was really delicious and Sana ate the full serving. Then they came outside and sat on the balcony. It was a lovely afternoon.

"So, shall I start, Sana?"

"Oh yes, Granny," replied Sana.

"Today, I will tell you about a very intelligent man. He was a prophet of God. Do you have any idea as to who this prophet was?"

"The Prophet Dawud (David)," replied Sana.

"Yes, he was a prophet blessed with intelligence. But today I will tell you about his son, the Prophet Sulaiman (Solomon). He was

unique as a prophet in the sense that Allah gave him the power to talk to animals and birds.

"Really, Granny, oh God, how lucky and blessed he was!"

"Yes, and he was also well known and respected for his wisdom. He was actually a man of many talents. He used to control the jinns and he had another talent; power over the wind. He was really good at making wise decisions. He made many wise decisions but, today, I will tell you about just two of these great decisions: the arguments of the mothers and the valley of the ants.

Firstly, I'll tell you about the mothers. There was a young woman and an elderly woman who used to live together. They loved their babies very much. But there was a very terrible happening one night when a wolf took away one of the babies. The women started arguing about whose baby was gone and whose was left. A lot of people gathered around them. One of them suggested that they should go to the Prophet Dawud (AS). After a lot of consideration, the Prophet Dawud (AS) decided that the baby should be given to the elderly woman, because, being older, she would be more reliable. The young woman did not agree to this, so they took the matter to the Prophet Sulaiman (AS).

After listening to both sides, he knew one of them was in the wrong. So he asked one of the servants to bring him a knife. He said that it would be fair to cut the baby into two pieces, so that each woman would get a part of the baby. Everyone was astonished. But the younger woman shouted that she was not the mother and she withdrew. Then the Prophet Sulaiman (AS) decided to give the baby to the younger mother, as only a mother could give up her own baby for its safety. Everyone was happy with the decision and the mother was thankful.

"Wow, he really knew human nature. I agree that only a mother could do a thing like that to protect her baby," said Sana.

"Now, let me tell you another very interesting incident. Once, the Prophet Sulaiman (AS) was travelling on a journey along with

his forces of jinns, birds and men. While they were on their way, they came across a valley known as the Valley of Ants. It is said that hundreds and thousands of ants used to live there. As the Prophet Sulaiman's army went through, the horses' hooves made a roaring sound as they touched the ground. The ants were really scared and went running here and there to save their lives. There was great chaos among the ants, as they did not know what to do. There was one ant that kept shouting and telling them to find shelter. The Prophet Sulaiman (AS) of course understood their language and smiled and thanked Allah for blessing him with this unique quality. He ordered his troops to stop marching. He then communicated to the king of the ants that the ants should not worry. When all the ants were safe and secure, the Prophet Sulaiman(AS) ordered his forces to continue on their way through the Valley of Ants."

"Amazing!" said Sana, quite mesmerised.

"Thank you, Granny, that was such a nice story." And she hugged her Granny.

"You are welcome, darling, and now we are getting late for the Asr prayer. Let us go inside and pray together," said Granny.

And they happily went inside the house where Sana was going to spend some more interesting and memorable days.

# Let's Think

## Lesson Learnt

Justice is very important in Islam and a leader should always be just and considerate to his people. Another important lesson is that intelligence is one of the most important of Allah's gifts, for it guides one towards a virtuous life.

## Verses from the Quran

We gave Solomon (Sulaiman) the right understanding of the matter, and We bestowed wisdom and knowledge on both of them. (21:79)

We subjected to Solomon the stormy wind, which blew at his behest towards the land, which We had blessed. For it is We who have knowledge of all things. We also subjected to him some of the jinn who dived for him in the sea and performed other tasks; We kept a watch over them. (21:81)

## Truth from the Hadith

Abu Hurayrah narrated that the Prophet said, 'Yesterday, a devil Jinn suddenly appeared to me, to interrupt me in my prayer. Then Allah made me powerful over him. And I wanted to fasten him with one of the pillars of the mosque so that you all see him in the morning. Then I recounted the prayer of my brother Sulaiman: 'My Lord, grant me such power, as no one after me will have. So I sent him back despicable.' (Al-Sahih Al Bukhari)

# The First Fast

## BY HIBAH HASSAN

Sparky was sitting on the stairs when he heard Malak's Mum's voice from Malak's room,

"Come on, Malak, you should go to bed early today. You know you have to get up very early tomorrow morning."

"Oh yes, Mum, I nearly forgot. Please wake me up in time for Sahoor (the meal before the fast)," replied Malak.

Then Malak's room door closed and Sparky heard no more.

"I wonder why Malak wants to get up early tomorrow. Maybe something exciting is going to happen," he thought to himself.

Then Sparky heard Malak's mother coming down the stairs so he followed her down as fast as his little kitty legs would carry him.

He walked into the kitchen and saw Ginger, an older cat, sitting on the windowsill. Sparky bounded over to the old cat and snuggled down next to him.

"You know, Ginger, tomorrow Malak is going to wake up really early, for Sahoor. But Ginger, what is Sahoor and why is Malak going to wake up so early?" asked Sparky.

"Well, tomorrow is the first day of Ramadhan. Ramadhan is the 9th month of the Islamic year. It is very special," replied Ginger

"But why is it so special? What happens during Ramadhan?" insisted the little kitten.

Ginger told Sparky that, during Ramadhan, Muslims woke up really early, before sunrise, they ate something and then throughout the rest of the day they did not eat or drink at all until sunset.

Sparky was very astonished to hear about fasting and he said, "Wow, they must get really hungry! Imagine not eating for the whole day. I'll bet it's really hard, right? But when there's no one watching them, I bet they can eat then!"

But Ginger replied confidently, "Well, actually, I heard Malak's Mum telling her that fasting is quite easy. You just have to believe that you can do it and then Allah surely helps you. And Sparky, there is always Allah watching us, wherever we are."

"Oh yes. I remember. Allah is All-seeing, All-hearing and the Greatest. Thanks for telling me all of this, Ginger," said Sparky, quickly.

So having thanked Ginger for telling him about Ramadhan, Sparky scampered off before Ginger could tell him about why Muslims fast during Ramadhan.

That night Sparky made up his mind to wake up early in the morning to watch Malak and her Mum. The little kitten fell fast asleep and was dreaming, when he heard Malak's alarm clock ringing. He quickly got out of bed and ran down to the kitchen. He watched Malak and her mother having fried eggs, toast and orange juice. He saw that Malak had finished eating, so he ran up to her and brushed against her knee.

"Oh Mum, look at Sparky, he wants to fast as well!" exclaimed Malak. Before her mother had time to reply, the loud Adhan (the call for prayer) for the dawn prayer, Fajr, resounded in the room. Malak and her mother said the Fajr prayer together and then went to bed.

When Malak woke up, she went downstairs to the kitchen to eat breakfast, but when Sparky saw this he remembered that Ginger had said, "They don't eat anything till sunset." So he ran to Malak and shook his head. But Malak didn't notice Sparky and was just about to put some jam on to her bread when Sparky started to miaow loudly. "That's funny, I'm sure that Sparky is trying to tell me something, I wonder what it is," said Malak out loud.

Malak's mother entered the kitchen and saw Malak spreading jam on to her bread and she reminded her softly, "Malak, have you forgotten? Today you are fasting. You can't eat anything. Remember?"

"Oh yes! I had completely forgotten, Mum. That must be what Sparky was trying to tell me! Clever Sparky!" exclaimed Malak.

"Well, Malak, Sparky isn't fasting, so remember to give him his breakfast now," said her mother.

But when Sparky's bowl had been filled with kitty nibble, Malak saw that Sparky didn't even touch his food. He didn't even take any notice of it.

"Oh dear, I hope Sparky isn't sick," thought Malak to herself.

Throughout the whole day, Malak remembered not to eat or drink anything. She was very proud of herself. At 5 o'clock, an hour and a half before sunset, the doorbell rang. Malak ran to answer it and saw that it was her friend Naomi.

Naomi was eating a packet of crisps and she offered Malak some crisps. Without thinking, Malak put her hand in the packet and put a crisp in her mouth. After she had swallowed it, she stopped for a second and burst into tears. Naomi was very surprised and said, "Malak, Malak, what's the matter? Is something wrong?" So between her tears, Malak explained to her about fasting and Ramadhan and that she wasn't supposed to eat anything.

Naomi felt very bad and they both ran to Malak's mother.

Mother hugged Malak and told her that, during fasting, if someone forgot and ate or drank anything by accident, no harm was done and the fast was not broken. She explained that Allah was very forgiving and merciful.

When Sparky heard that 'it was an accident', he ran off to find Ginger. He found Ginger in the back yard and he asked him why it didn't matter if 'it was an accident'. Ginger explained to him that Malak had eaten by accident, so it didn't matter. Allah was all forgiving and merciful.

69

"Sparky, do you know why Muslims fast in Ramadhan?" asked Ginger.

"Yes, I know, it's because Allah told Muslims to," replied Sparky.

"That's true, but do you know why Allah wants Muslims to fast?" asked Ginger.

"No, I don't" replied Sparky innocently.

"It's because Allah wants people to realise how the poor and needy feel without food and then they can help them," explained Ginger.

"Oh, I understand now," said Sparky happily and he gave Ginger a big hug.

This time Sparky had learned the whole lesson about Ramadhan and he went back to his basket much wiser than before.

At home, everyone made a great fuss over him. Malak was nearly in tears when she saw that her kitten had not touched his food or his water at breakfast or lunch. She ran to her mother and told her about Sparky.

She was reassured by her mother's caring words. "Do not worry about Sparky, he'll be fine. We'll take him to the vet tomorrow."

The time came for Malak and her Mother to break their fasts. Both of them sat together and said their duaas and prayed to Allah.

They broke their fast by eating dates and drinking water. Malak knew that it was good to break the fast with dates and water, because that was how the Prophet Muhammad (pbuh) had broken his fasts.

Then Malak's mother went into the kitchen to get the other food she had prepared and saw that Sparky was finally eating his food and drinking water, so she called Malak into the kitchen and said, "Look at Sparky, Malak, isn't it funny how he is eating now?"

"Oh Mummy, I understand now, we were not the only ones fasting, Sparky was fasting too!" said the delighted Malak.

She then said the evening prayer, Maghrib, and played with Sparky for the rest of the evening. When it was night time, Malak went to sleep with a huge smile on her face.

That day was a very special day in Malak's home, for it was Malak's first fast and it was Sparky's as well.

# Let's Think

### Lesson Learnt
The story shows how important fasting is in Islam, it is one of the five pillars and it helps us to be grateful to Allah for what he has blessed us with. Fasting is a lot of fun and your first fast can be very rewarding!

### Verses from the Quran
Believers, fasting has been prescribed for you, just as it was prescribed for those before you, so that you may guard yourselves against evil (2:183)

### Truth from the Hadith
Abu Huraira related that the Prophet (pbuh) said: Whoever fasts during Ramadhan with faith and seeking his reward from Allah will have his past sins forgiven. (Bukhari)

# The Runaway Hamster
## BY HAYA HASSAN

Zaina lived in a big house with her Mum, her Dad and a pet hamster named 'Spotty'. Zaina, who was nine years of age, had black hair and brown eyes. She was very kind but quite lazy. One day when Zaina woke up, her Mum called her downstairs for breakfast. It was already very late and Zaina was, as usual, the last one out of bed.

"Mum, can I eat upstairs because I want to watch TV?" shouted Zaina.

"Okay, but don't drop anything," replied Mum. "And Zaina, do remember to feed your hamster," Mum called.

Zaina ran into her room, put a tiny bit of food in her hamster's bowl and ran to watch TV. Zaina had the very bad habit of always watching TV. She wasn't very active and spent most of the day in front of the television set.

Zaina was a very lucky girl, because she had a lovely creamy white, fluffy, little hamster called Spotty. When Zaina had first brought Spotty from the pet shop, he was very healthy. He was very fast and was always playing in his cage tunnels.

But after some days, Zaina lost interest and didn't play so much with her hamster and used to often forget him. Very often Zaina even forgot to feed her hamster. Day by day, Spotty got thinner and thinner.

When Zaina noticed that Spotty wasn't running or playing in his cage any more, she was worried about him but, as usual, she got busy watching her favourite TV programme and forgot all about him. One night Zaina forgot to close Spotty's cage door and he leapt out of his cage in search of food. When everyone was still and silent, Spotty was scampering about the whole house.

He explored Zaina's room and when he saw that the door of the room was open, he quickly ran out. Suddenly, Spotty found himself looking down at the staircase. He was just about to take his first step down the stairs when he saw a picture of the family cat hanging on the wall.

Spotty was scared out of his life! He squeaked and started running in circles. Suddenly he found himself tumbling down the stairs. 'Bump, bump, bump.' Poor Spotty! He was rolling down the stairs very quickly, but he was glad to get away from the horrible, scary cat upstairs.

Spotty explored the whole house. In the kitchen the cupboard was not tightly shut. So he squeezed himself inside and jumped on to the shelf. To his surprise, right in front of him was a whole packet

of hamster food! He immediately dived into the packet and started gobbling down the food.

When he was full, he ran into the living room and curled up behind the cosy sofa and fell fast asleep.

The next morning, the first one to wake up was Zaina's Dad. He had to wake up very early to go to his office. He tiptoed into the kitchen, ate breakfast and then went into the living room to fetch his keys. He picked up his heavy car keys but they accidentally slipped out of his hand and fell behind the sofa.

The startled Spotty woke up seeing a huge hand coming towards him. When Zaina's Dad reached out to grab his keys, he felt something soft and furry in his hands. He recognised the ball of fluff to be Zaina's thin little hamster.

"Hmm, that's funny. I thought that Spotty was asleep in his cage. I wonder how he escaped?" said the puzzled Dad.

When Zaina woke up at 10.30 in the morning, she couldn't find Spotty. They all looked everywhere but there was no sign of the little hamster.

Zaina kept looking for Spotty and crying all day until Dad came home. "I know where your hamster is," said Dad. "I gave it to someone who will look after him properly."

The next day began the weekend. Zaina was very sad. Zaina and her family were invited to dinner at the house of Uncle Usman, a very good friend of her Dad. Half-heartedly, Zaina went with her family to dinner. To her surprise, her hamster, Spotty was running about and playing with Uncle Usman's son, Ahmed.

Zaina ran to her Dad and said angrily,

"Why is my hamster in their house?"

Dad calmed her down and replied, "You didn't look after your hamster properly."

"But that's not fair, it's my hamster!" cried Zaina.

"Zaina, do you notice how Spotty is looking so happy and so much healthier? Do you know why?" asked Dad.

Zaina realised her Dad was right. Spotty did look healthier and much more active than before.

"Spotty is happy here, as he is fed in time and the kids spend time playing with him," said the Dad.

Meanwhile, Uncle Usman noticed Zaina was upset and he called everyone for dinner. Zaina forgot about Spotty as a delicious smell of pizza was coming from kitchen. She joined the family at the dining table. As Zaina finished her dinner, she remembered it was time for her favourite cartoon. She said to Ahmed, "Hey, it's time for 'Tom and Jerry'. Let's go and watch it."

Ahmed didn't know much about cartoons and showed no interest. Instead, he asked Zaina to come and see his new paintings in his room.

Zaina went with him upstairs to see the paintings. She was surprised to see the children's room. It was beautifully decorated with lovely drawings and paintings.

"Who made them?" asked the surprised Zaina.

"I did," replied Ahmed. "Do you like paintings? We can paint something, if you like."

Zaina didn't know what to say. She spent most of her spare time watching TV and never tried to do anything else.

"Maybe I can try along with you," replied Zaina.

They both took out the paints and paper and, with Ahmed's help. Zaina drew a lovely picture and painted it neatly.

She was having a lot of fun and forgot all about TV.

Dad and uncle Usman came upstairs; Zaina happily showed them her picture. They both liked it and appreciated Zaina's efforts.

"Its time to go home, Zaina," said Dad.

Zaina came downstairs and saw her hamster in the living room. She was very sad and had tears in her eyes.

She asked her father, "Please Dad, I promise I won't spend so much time on TV. I'll look after my hamster. So can we take him back home?"

Uncle Usman stepped forward and said to Zaina's Dad, "I think Zaina has learnt her lesson and I am sure she will look after her hamster."

Zaina hugged her father and pleaded "Please, please, Dad, I promise."

Mum said to Zaina, "You know it's a big responsibility to keep pets. The Prophet Muhammad (pbuh) always emphasised that we should be kind to animals and was once very angry with a woman who didn't look after her cat."

Dad, realising that Zaina was ashamed and sorry for her carelessness, allowed her to take her hamster back home. Dad also promised Ahmed he would get him a new hamster.

# Let's Think

## Lesson Learnt

We learn two important lessons from this story:

We should spend our time in meaningful things rather than wasting it on useless TV programmes.

Keeping pets is nice but we should take good care of them, play with them and be responsible for their well being.

## Verses from the Quran

I swear by the passage of time, that man is surely in a state of loss, except for those who believe and do good deeds and exhort one another to hold fast to the Truth, and who exhort one another to steadfastness. (103:1-3)

## Truth from the Hadith

"There are two blessings, which many people lose: they are health and free time for doing good." (Bukhari)

The Prophet Muhammad (pbuh) told his Companions of a woman who would be sent to Hell for having locked up a cat not feeding it, nor even releasing it so that it could feed herself. (Bukhari)

# Halloween

## BY ZINEB SARAH MESSAOUI

It was Amira's first day at school and she was very excited. She and her parents had just moved into the area. It had been hard to choose a school, as her father wanted a private Muslim girl's school. But as it had been too expensive, they just sent her to the closest public school.

She came into her class: 6B.

Her teacher, Mrs. Williams introduced her to the students. "Class, here is the new girl, Amira Salaah. I hope you will all be very kind to her."

Mrs. Williams put Amira next to another girl named Safa.

"Hi, I'm Safa. If you need anything, just ask me," she said. "Okay," said Amira shyly.

In one week Amira and Safa had become great friends and Amira felt less shy. She found out that Safa was a Muslim and that she lived not very far away from Amira.

One October morning, at playtime, a girl from Amira's class gave everybody an invitation to her Halloween party.

"It's a Halloween party!" exclaimed Amira frowning. "Yeah, Halloween parties are such fun. We have plenty of spooky party

games and then we usually watch scary films," replied Safa excitedly.

"But Safa, in Islam it is forbidden to celebrate Halloween or any such thoughtless activities," said Amira, shocked. "Aren't you a Muslim?" she asked.

Safa looked uncomfortable and said in a small voice, "There's nothing wrong in celebrating Halloween," and she walked away.

That afternoon Amira explained the problem to her mother. "I don't know what to do to convince her that going to that party is wrong," she cried out.

"Well, you see, Amira darling, sometimes many Muslims are not aware of the facts behind certain celebrations, so they think that they are all right. In her heart maybe she knows its wrong but she doesn't want to feel different from the other children by not going to the party," her mother explained kindly.

"Well, what can we do?" asked Amira desperately.

"I know," said Amira's Mum, and she whispered something in her daughter's ear.

The next day Amira came to school with some papers in her hand. She asked the teacher if she could use the story telling area that day. So, at playtime she gathered all the children together at the story telling area.

"I am going to read you something about Halloween that I looked up on the Internet. It will benefit us all, InshaAllah," said Amira, and then she started:

"Halloween is a celebration of Celtic people who worshipped many gods. They believed that on the eve of the Celtic New Year, which is for us October 31, the souls of the dead people roam the land of the living. The Devil, spirits and witches were also believed to be moving about on broomsticks and could harm the people with their power.

"We all know that only God has all the powers. A dead person can neither give us anything nor harm us," said Amira.

"Let me tell you about the Halloween activities.

"Do you know why they dress up in fancy costumes?" asked Amira.

"Yes I know," replied one of the kids. "It's to have fun and to look nice."

"No, it's not only that. Dressing up in costumes was done so that the spirits would not recognise people and would not harm them. Today, children who dress up represent these spirits.

"Do you like trick and treating?" asked Amira

"Oh yes, it's so much fun and you get lots of candies," exclaimed Safa.

"Actually, the spirits would go from house to house on October 31 to ask for food. The people who didn't give them any were cursed, so to avoid being cursed, the people gave them food or candies. We all know none of this is true.

So Halloween is actually the celebration of the false gods of the olden days. Do we believe in those gods who never existed? All of you should think before participating in the celebration of the devil, of ghosts, of imaginary witches and of superstitions," she ended emphatically.

On that word, all the children stood up and promised never to celebrate Halloween ever again.

Safa hugged Amira with tears in her eyes "Thank you for making me understand the truth behind Halloween… thank you," she said. From then on all the children kept their promises. They even made a club and learnt about Islam together.

# Let's Think

## Lesson Learnt

One should not celebrate Halloween, as it is a festival from the religion of the Celts. In this religion they celebrated the devil and did not believe in the one true god, Allah. A Muslim just believes in one God and follows the path shown by Him. Allah is all powerful. A Muslim should always think before he does anything.

## Verses from the Quran

And do not eat anything over which God's name has not been pronounced, for that surely is disobedience. The devils inspire their followers to argue with you. If you obey them, you will become of those who associate partners with God. (6:121)

## Truth from the Hadith

Anas (ra), a companion of the Prophet Muhammad (pbuh) reported that when the Prophet Muhammad (pbuh) migrated from Makkah to Madinah, the people of Madinah used to have two festivals. On those two days they had carnivals and festivity. The Prophet Muhammad (pbuh) told them: 'Instead of those two days, Allah has appointed two other days of festival which are better, the days of Eid-al-Fitr and Eid-al-Adha.' (Sahih Muslim)

The Prophet (pbuh) said: "Whoever imitates a people is one of them." (Abu Dawood)

# The Lollipops
## BY AMEENA GOLDING

It was a nice, sunny day in Ashville, and Sarah and some of her friends were out shopping in Ashville's massive shopping mall. Suddenly, one of Sarah's friends, Rebecca, spotted a sweetie shop that sold loads of tasty sweets, like bonbons, pear drops and sherbet lemons. Immediately, the girls rushed into the shop, as they were hungry and all the sweets looked so delicious! From the corner of her eye, Sarah could see another one of her friends, Samina grab a couple of lollipops and shove them into her pocket, when no one was looking! "She hasn't even paid for them!" Sarah thought to herself. She tried to forget about it, so she bought some toffees and waited

outside for her friends. When her friends finally came out, Sarah noticed that her friend's pockets were bulging with something. "What's that in your pockets?" Sarah asked her friends. "Sweets, duh!" they replied. "I didn't know you had any money left. I thought you spent it all on clothes!" Sarah said in a sort of whisper. "Of

course we don't have any money. We just took the lollies and left before anyone saw us," Samina whispered in Sarah's ear. "But that's stealing!" Sarah exclaimed! "Well, it was only once, and it's only one lollypop," Samina lied. "I guess..." Sarah trailed off, as she joined the group.

Two days later...

Sarah twiddled around with her pencil as she waited for her teacher, Mrs. Harrow, to start the class's little song, a vow that they had made up a few weeks ago. The chant started: "I promise to obey God, to serve my parents, take care of my family and always to be honest, truthful..." As soon as Sarah heard the word 'honest', her mind rushed back to two days ago when she was in the mall with her friends. Suddenly, Sarah realised that what her friends had done was wrong in Islam as well. As soon as she got home, she said her Asr prayer and asked Allah to forgive her for being foolish and doing something, which was not correct. The next day, Sarah confronted her friends and told them that what they had done was wrong and recited to them a verse from the Quran: "Do not mix up wrong with right, nor conceal the truth on purpose. The believers will win." Sarah also explained to her friends that stealing was wrong and that they could end up in jail for stealing, but more importantly that stealing was forbidden in Islam!" Sarah's friends suddenly realised what they had done, and that it was wrong. "Sarah, we had no idea that stealing was such a grave sin in Islam. We were just doing it for a bit of fun, but now we realise how serious it is. We all promise that we'll never steal again," said Samina quietly. All the friends said the chant together. "We promise to obey God, serve our parents, and take care of our families and always to be honest and truthful."

The next day, the friends went to the mall again. They also went to the sweetie shop. This time they also paid for the sweets, which they had earlier stolen, their favourite rainbow lollies, and this time they tasted even sweeter.

# Let's Think

## Lesson Learnt
Always be truthful, because even if nobody can see you, Allah always can. Stealing is a grave sin.

## Verses from the Quran
Do not mix truth with falsehood, or hide the truth when you know it. (2:42).

Do not consume one another's property by unjust means,
Nor offer it as a bribe to the authorities, so that you may
Deliberately and wrongfully devour a part of other people's wealth. (2:188)

## Truth from the Hadith
Ubada ibn as-Samit said, "We were with the Prophet(pbuh), in a gathering. He said, 'Give me allegiance on the basis, that you will not associate anything with Allah, will not steal. And whoever fulfils his pledge his reward is with Allah". (Bukhari)

# You Can Still Be a Winner

## BY XENEB SHAH

It was New Year's eve again. "I wonder if this year will be better for me," thought Dania while getting ready for school.

"Dania, your school bus is here," said her Mom.

"Mo...m, are you su...re, it won't be a ba...d year?" asked Dania anxiously.

"Oh yes, Insha Allah, it will be the best year of your life, darling. Now quick or you'll be late for school."

"Hello, welcome," said the new bus driver.

Dania just smiled, because she didn't want him to know that she stammered, otherwise he would laugh at her and also make fun of her."

She sat next to a girl who had lots of curls, but she didn't ask her name. Besides, the girl was not paying any attention as she was sleeping.

The day went off very well. The teacher only distributed the books and took the attendance. School ended quickly.

But the next day was not that easy for little Dania. The teacher asked her to read a paragraph and the whole class started laughing as she read with great difficulty. The teacher was not kind either. Instead of scolding the children, she asked Dania rudely to stop in the middle. Soon it was break time. Dania came out of the class sadly and started crying. She cried so hard that there was a puddle of tears, but no one really cared for her. After the recess, she went back to the class and found the same curly haired girl sitting in the corner of the class. She sat beside her and felt confused, but that girl was kind enough not to ask her anything, or perhaps she was still sleepy.

"I could hang around with her. She is lazy enough not to notice my speech," thought Dania.

She came back home and told her Mom about the incident in class. She wanted her Mom to complain to the school about the teacher's rude behaviour.

"But Dania, we are Muslims and don't you think we should try to forgive others for their bad behaviour and pray to Allah to give us power to ignore such behaviour? Now, when you pray your regular salaat, do ask Allah to help you improve your speech."

"Yes, Mom, you a…re.. Right. I sho…uld pray hard. And wha…t about my sp..eech therapy?"

"Yes, Dania, we are looking for the best therapist and we might take you abroad," replied her Mum.

It was a normal school day when the teacher announced that there would be a speech competition. All the big schools were participating. The topic was 'How we should treat children with different abilities.' Now this was the topic Dania could write pages and pages on, but to deliver the speech was not an easy job for the poor child.

Dania started working hard for the speech. She did not tell anyone

in the class except for the curly haired girl who was now her friend. At least she was not like the others who used to make a fool of her. So what if she was lazy?

The night before the competition Dania was very tense.

Her Mom asked Dania, "Did I ever tell you about Helen Keller?"

"No, wha..t is sp...ecial about her?"

"She was blind and deaf, but she was a brave person. She became the first blind and deaf person to get a Bachelor of Arts degree. Then she became a writer and she worked for the poor and blind people.

"Oh, how bra...ve she was! I am impr...essed Mommy," said Dania.

"I am telling you her story because you are much better than her. So have courage and do your best tomorrow and don't forget to pray and ask Allah's help. I'm sure He will be on your side tomorrow," said her Mom.

This gave Dania new hope and she prayed with all her heart and revised her speech.

Dania entered the school hall with a nervous look on her face, but soon she felt better. Then it was her turn to deliver the speech.

She started her speech with the following words.

"Mr. Presi...dent, to...day is my d..ay. I am sure no one will laugh at my sta......mmering, as the to....pic of the day is about treating kids like me. I would be thankful if you ign....ored my stammering and just considered the content of my spee....ch."

Guess what! When she had finished her speech. The curly haired girl stood up and started clapping and then everyone else did the same. Her rude teacher hugged her and told her that her speech was the speech of the day.

Finally the result was announced and Dania got a special prize. She could not believe it. She ran to the stage to get her prize and her Mom thanked Allah for His kindness

# Let's Think

## Lesson Learnt

Allah made us all different with different talents. We should always try to do our best and ask help from Allah. We should always be thankful to Allah for all His blessings.

## Verses from the Quran

If God helps you, none can overcome you, but if He withdraws His help from you, who is there who can help you besides Him? In God, then, let the believers place their trust! (3:160)

## Truth from the Hadith

"If you all relied on Allah with due reliance, He would certainly give you provision as He gives it to birds who issue forth hungry in the morning and return with full belly at dusk." (At-Tirmidhi)

# Skin Colour

## BY ZINEB SARAH MESSAOUI

Hamid had been pleading with his Dad to let him get enrolled in Evolution Soccer, a football club. Finally he had agreed and Hamid felt so excited. "Hamid, what are you doing? Get downstairs, otherwise we'll be late!" called his Dad.

Hamid rushed downstairs, missing the last step and falling down. "Are you okay, Hamid?" asked his Mum, worried,

"Yes, Mum, I'm just really excited," he replied, smiling.

He jumped into the car and his Dad sped down the lane. He dropped Hamid off, kissed him and zoomed off. Hamid, now realising that he didn't know anyone there, felt a bit shy. He went up to a man at the administration.

"I'm enrolled in the club, in the fifth group with referee Joe Mainer," he said in a small voice.

The man took the paper that Hamid handed him and then took him to a big football field, where there were already a lot of children.

"Here's Hamid Abdulkarim," said the man, pronouncing his last

name with a lot of difficulty. The boys laughed, as they thought that the name was strange. Hamid felt himself blushing

"Hi, I hope we'll all be friends and will have good games together," said Hamid, trying to sound confident.

The boys ignored him and looked away.

"Hey, is that sunburn or were you born like that?" asked one of the boys, pointing to his face.

Hamid, who was from Pakistan, had darker skin compared to the other boys.

He decided not to answer the rude boy's question. He ignored the boys for the following days and concentrated on football. As the days followed, the boys kept teasing him. They even invented a nickname for him: "Curry".

Adam, a tall boy, who was the leader of the group of boys, was the one who teased Hamid the most. He was a European and thought people who were different were not as good as white people or people like him. "We don't want any of your races, Curry," he said to him.

"So you admit that you're a racist!" said Hamid, angrily.

The boys kept on ignoring him. One day, Hamid felt that it was too much. He was very sad and helpless, so he decided to consult the Quran and seek God's guidance. In it he found a verse that he thought was guidance from God that how he should handle his problems. He was happy and very grateful to God. The verse was:

"Good deeds and evil deeds are not equal. Return evil with good, and he who is your enemy will become your dearest friend. But none will attain this attribute save those who patiently endure; none will attain it save those who are truly fortunate." (41:34, 35)

Since then this verse became his guideline in his interaction with anyone who was bad with him. So, over the next few days Hamid tried to be very kind to the other players, even if they were annoying. Joe, a short boy, fell down when an opponent pushed him. His knee was bleeding and the other boys didn't know what to do. Hamid helped him up and washed his cut with soap to make sure it wouldn't get infected. Joe, didn't resist, he looked at him and found his knee healed quickly.

"Wow, how did you know what to do?" asked Joe in awe.

"Well, in Pakistan, my grandmother used to teach us how to wash cuts and cure people so that we could help her, as she is the village healer," said Hamid, smiling.

"Thanks a lot," Joe smiled back.

Hamid was happy to have made a friend at last, but still, the other boys pretended not to be impressed and ignored him. Day by day, Hamid tried to show the boys that he is as good as they are and he continued to be helpful. One day, the referee accused Adam of paying the opponents to let him score more goals. Hamid knew very well that Adam hated the other team's captain, a long, skinny boy named William. Hamid remembered one day when the two boys had fought and had vowed to have nothing to do with each other again. So, Hamid explained to the referee that Adam wasn't responsible for what he was being accused of. Hamid gave him proof by bringing along a boy who had witnessed the fight between William and Adam. This convinced the referee. He apologised to Adam and left the boys together.

"Thank you!" whispered Adam, weakly. "But, since you came here, I've been humiliating you and annoying you. Still, you helped me... Why?" Adam asked amazed.

"Well, you see…" said Hamid humbly "My religion, Islam, teaches me to forgive everyone, even if they have been very mean to us," he explained.

Adam seemed to go pale; he simply couldn't understand how someone could be so forgiving. The two boys walked over to the rest of the team silently. Adam stood on an old box (where any boy could stand if he had an important announcement to make).

He gathered up all his courage and finally said: "We boys have been unjust and horribly racist to a certain boy standing amongst us. But still this boy tried again and again to make friends with us. He helped Joe, when he cut his knee, was honest and forgave us for the terrible things we said and did. I suggest we should all apologise to him for all the pain and humiliation we caused him. This boy is Hamid… And anybody who wants to annoy him again will have to answer to me!" he finished angrily.

"I'm really sorry and ashamed of having been racist towards you, Hamid," said Jim humbly.

"I apologise for my meanness," added another boy.

"Sorry," said another.

All the boys started apologising and admitting they were wrong.

They all admired Hamid's persistence, courage and, of course his willingness to forgive. They all decided to make him the gang's leader, but Hamid refused:

"I just wanted to show you that all human beings, even if they are of a different country or colour, are all equal. What actually makes a difference between two people is not how they are on the outside or what their surroundings are like, but how good they are in their hearts and in their deeds." The boys all cheered as he finished what he had to say. They had all learnt their lesson and were never racist ever again.

# Let's Think

## Lesson Learnt

We must not judge people by how they look or where they come from but by the kindness of their hearts and their deeds.

## Verses from the Quran

Mankind! We have created you from a male and female, and made you into peoples and tribes, so that you might come to know each other. The noblest of you in God's sight is the one who fears God most. God is all-knowing and all-aware. (49:13)

## Truth from the Hadith

"All mankind is from Adam and Eve. An Arab has no superiority over a non-Arab. Neither does a non-Arab have any superiority over an Arab. Also, a white person has no superiority over a black person. Neither does a black person have any superiority over a white person - except by piety and good action." (Bukhari)

# I Love You Mummy
## BY HIBAH HASSAN

Yahya had just come back from Sunday school. He always had lots of fun there but today was extra special because his teacher had told him the story of Sharaf al Din. When Yahya got home he saw his younger brother Zain, who was five, playing with the train set.

"Zain! Zain, sit down with me and I will tell you a really good story about a boy called Sharaf al-din."

So Zain sat down next to his brother and listened eagerly.

And Yahya began his story, "Sharaf was a very kind boy and he loved and cared for his parents. He always listened to them and was happy to serve them. One day, Sharaf's mother was nearly asleep and felt thirsty. So she asked Sharaf to get her a glass of water. Sharaf was very happy to get her water. But when he got back to his mother's room he found her fast asleep.

Sharaf did not want to disturb her, he said to himself, Mum had a long day and she needs to rest I shouldn't wake her up.

"Oh that was very kind of him!" said Zain jumping up and down in excitement.

"And Zain, Well he stood next to his mother for a very long time, thinking that when she woke she would still be thirsty. So Sharaf waited and waited until finally she woke up."

"Oh my dear son, have you been waiting all this time?"

"Yes mother" replied Sharaf lovingly. "I wanted you to have water as soon as you woke up."

His mother was very touched and blessed Sharaf for his kindness. And you know Allah was so happy with Sharaf that when he grew up, he was a very famous man, Sheikh Sharaf al-din, the famous scholar…. The end".

"Did you like it Zain?" asked Yahya.

"Oh yes!" exclaimed Zain.

Yahya and Zain happily went outside to play.

The next day, Yahya was at school and Zain was at home. Zain was very bored, he had played with all his toys, he had played with the cat and he also had drawn some pictures.

Zain was sitting on the couch doing nothing when he remembered the story of Sharaf Al Din. Zain suddenly had an idea and he ran to his mothers room. His mother was sitting on the bed reading a book when Zain came in.

"Mummy, Mummy go to sleep," asked Zain.

His mother was puzzled by her son's request but she had only a chapter left till her book was finished so she said,

"Wait a minute Zain, let me just finish this …"

"No, no Mummy just please, please go to sleep!" pleaded Zain.

"But Zain," his mother said, but when she saw that Zain would not go until she slept, she laid down, closed her eyes and pretended to snore. But Zain was not satisfied. "Mummy, are you thirsty?" he asked.

"No darling, I just drank a cup of tea five minutes ago," replied his mother.

"No Mummy, you have to be thirsty, say you are thirsty Mummy, please Mummy," said Zain impatiently.

"Okay Zain, I am 'thirsty'," his mother gave in.

Zain ran downstairs and fetched a glass of water. He hid the glass behind his back and insisted that his mother should sleep again. His mother wanted to understand what Zain wanted, so she pretended to sleep again. She closed her eyes and waited, the room was silent. Zain stood there with the glass of water not wanting to disturb his mother. After few minutes she opened one eye and said, "Can I open my eyes now Zain?"

"Well, okay Mummy and here is your glass of water, and now Allah is happy with me like he was with Sharaf!"

Zain's mother finally understood Zain and smiled. She hugged Zain and took him on her lap and said, "Of course, Zain Allah is very happy with you Allah loves the children who care for and respect their parents".

Zain was very happy to hear this.

Mum added, "Zain, you know the meaning of Sharaf's story is that, children should always listen to their parents and take care of them as Mum and Dad take care of them when they are children. Allah is very happy with obedient children just like you Zain, who never shout or disrespect their parents. Allah loves us very much and wants us to be always good."

Zain hugged his mother and said, "I love you Mummy."

# Let's Think

## Lesson Learnt

We should always be very kind and respectful to our parents. We should never forget it was our parents who raised us with warmth and love and took care of us. It is now our turn to show love and kindness to them.

## Verses from the Quran

We have enjoined man to show kindness to his parents-

For his mother bears him, in hardship upon hardship, and his weaning takes two years. [We said] Give thanks to Me and to your parents; all will return to Me. (31:14)

We have enjoined man to show kindness to his parents. (29:8)

## Truth from the Hadith

A man came to the Prophet and said, "O Messenger of God! Who among the people is the most worthy of my good companionship? The Prophet replied, 'Your mother'. The man said, 'Then who?' The Prophet replied, 'Your mother'. The man further asked, 'Then who?' The Prophet replied, 'Your mother'. The man asked again, 'Then who?' The Prophet replied 'Then your father'". (Bukhari, Muslim).

# Meet the Authors

My name is Ameena Golding and I'm 12 years old. I live in England, so I speak English, but I also speak Spanish and a little Arabic. Some of my hobbies and interests include reading, swimming, cooking, cycling, playing the piano and arts and crafts. I have a hamster named Chi-chi and he's so funny! I loved writing these stories and I hope you like reading them too!

My name is Haya Hassan and I am 10 years old. I was born in Karachi, Pakistan, and have lived in Saudi Arabia and England. Currently, I am living in Cairo with my family. I love to travel and visit different places. My hobbies are swimming, bike riding and travelling. I also enjoy reading and writing stories, especially about animals. I hope you'll enjoy my stories.

My name is Hibah Hassan; I'm 12 years old, of Pakistani origin, and am a British citizen. I have lived in England, Saudi Arabia, and Pakistan and am currently living in Cairo. I have been to many other countries and I get most of my ideas from the different cultures, places and people I have seen. My hobbies include reading, gardening, baking, arts and crafts and horse riding. And I love animals! I really enjoyed writing stories for this book and I hope you will enjoy reading them!

I am Xeneb Shah. I was born in the City of Karachi, Pakistan, in 1998. I had my early schooling in Pakistan. Two years ago, we moved to Cairo as my father was transferred to Egypt. I am now in grade six. I am running a book club at school, which is one of the most popular clubs of the school. My hobbies include book reading, bike riding and playing tennis. My dream is to become a very popular author. I hope you will enjoy my stories.

My name is Zineb Sarah Messaoui. I was born on September 9, 1998, at Marseilles, France, and lived there till I was two years old. Then I lived in Swindon in England for seven years. Then I moved to Doha, the capital of Qatar, where I'm living now. I've always wanted to write stories. But I never thought I would get a chance like this. I hope all of you will enjoy my stories.

# Bringing you a splendid range of Islamic books and children's products

Here for young readers and listeners, are all the best treasured stories of the Quran in one beautifully illustrated volume. The stirring and dramatic stories of the great prophets, peoples and nations are unfolded as a family saga, one event leading naturally to the next.

A fascinating handbook to all the key people in the Quran. Find out Quran's most important people; Discover the strengths and weaknesses of the people of the Quran; Locate the Quranic passages on key people; Learn the meaning and message of the stories from the Quran.

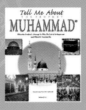

The book presents the life of the Prophet Muhammad, upon whom be peace, from his childhood in the desert to his divine mission and early preaching in Makkah.

The answers to every child's longing to hear a good bedtime story.

● A simple text

● Fabulous colour illustrations

The book offers a special dimension to these wonderful goodnight stories.

Professor Abdur Rahim's eight-volume series of textbooks enable the student to acquire a knowledge of Arabic in the classical structural form. All the books teach essential language skills through applied grammar.

This course teaches young students comprehensive Islamic education, comprising general Islamic knowledge based on the Quran and Hadith. The course includes Quranic text, followed by exercises.

Two tale sets of the Quran's best loved stories down the generations, that can be clearly understood and are fun to read, share and enjoy. Their texts are the perfect gateway to to your children's lifetime adventure of reading from the Quran.

## New Releases...

# GOODWORD

info@goodwordbooks.com
goodwordbooks.com
goodword.net